the
double-edged sword

the
double-edged sword

An evidence-informed workbook for the well-being of nurses and the places they work.

Corey S. Pressman, MA, CCFP, CTP
Brylee Kiminski, BS
Chloé Littzen-Brown, PhD, RN

AMERICAN NURSES ASSOCIATION

About the American Nurses Association

The American Nurses Association (ANA) is the only full-service professional organization representing the interests of the nation's 4.3 million registered nurses through its constituent/state nurses associations and its organizational affiliates. The ANA advances the nursing profession by fostering high standards of nursing practice, promoting the rights of nurses in the workplace, projecting a positive and realistic view of nursing, and by lobbying the Congress and regulatory agencies on health care issues affecting nurses and the public.

American Nurses Association
8515 Georgia Avenue, Suite 400
Silver Spring, MD 20910

Library of Congress Cataloging-in-Publication Data Available on Request

ISBNs
print 9781953985682
epdf 9781953985699
epub 9781953985705
mobi 9781953985712

Published in the United States of America

1 2 3 4 5   27 26 25 24 23

CONTENTS

Disclaimer   vii

Foreword by Dr. Jennifer Mensik   ix

About the Authors   xi

Famous by Naomi Shihab Nye   xii

1   **Introduction** 1

2   **Subjective Vitality** 7

3   **Emotional Regulation** 23

4   **Vital Compassion** 33

5   **Vital Organizations** 43

A   **References and Recommended Readings for Vital Practice** . .51

DISCLAIMER

This book details available evidenced-based strategies to be implemented by professionals and leadership teams within healthcare organizations where nurses work. The statements, strategies, activities, and other content are provided on an as-is basis to be used as a guiding resource for the reader. They are not intended to diagnose, treat, or cure any condition or disease relating to mental, physical, or emotional health. This book is not intended or designed to replace a healthcare provider should one be required. Please consult with your own physician or mental health specialist regarding the suggestions and recommendations made in this book.

Furthermore, the authors do not suggest this book as a self-help resource to be used in extreme situations. **If you are in crisis or think you may be having a mental health emergency,**

* Call your doctor or 911 immediately.
* Call 988 if you're having suicidal thoughts to talk to a skilled, trained counselor at a crisis center in your area at any time (National Suicide and Crisis Lifeline).
* Call your local emergency line immediately if you are located outside the United States.
* Connect with a mental health specialist within your organization or local area who is licensed to provide care to you on a more individualized and long-term basis.

This book provides content related to the promotion of physical and mental well-being. As such, the use of this book implies your acceptance of this disclaimer.

—Authors of *The Double-Edged Sword* and
American Nurses Association Publishing Team

FOREWORD

I first met Dr Chloe Littzen as a brand-new nurse who took on a position within the community right after graduation. Chloe demonstrated her strong desire to help others from the start. Through her own journey of professional and personal development, she shared her own stories and challenges with self-care and illness with friends and colleagues. Her reflective practices and education had an important bearing on my own self-care journey with my autoimmune diseases. This prompted me to be more mindful and to incorporate more self-care into my daily life.

Partnering with Corey Pressman and Brylee Kiminski on this vitally important topic, Chloe and her colleagues share their insight, knowledge, and experience to help you on your own journey of well-being, and to become compassionate to yourself, not just your patients.

In my role as President of the American Nurses Association, I am blessed with the opportunity to talk to nurses everywhere. I have heard and seen firsthand that the most important issue facing our profession right now is well-being and our own self-care. Nurses throughout our country, and indeed around the globe, are dealing with chronic stress. This needs to change for all of us. As we learn more, we now understand that post-traumatic stress syndrome (PTSD) is not always caused by one single event, but instead can result from continued stressful events that we do not process.

As I reflected on my own self-care journey, I realized that I do not remember anyone ever teaching me about this in my undergraduate or graduate education. In fact, I think I learned how to be more stressed than ever. I know that if I wasn't taught, in my nursing education, about compassionate care, about self-care, then surely our colleagues who are not nurses, who are executives in our organizations, wouldn't have learned this either.

But thankfully this is changing, and it is changing with this book. One nurse at a time. You. And as you read this book, do not apply the learnings to only yourself. Share this with colleagues, your manager, and others. If you are a manager, make this a responsibility of your position and change your unit or department culture. Provide this book to your staff so they can incorporate these ideas into everyday practice, staff meetings, employee check-ins, and how they lead. It will take all of us in every position to change the culture and make compassionate care a way of being for everyone, patients, nurses, and staff.

Self-care is different for each of us, and this book will help you find what that means to you and how you can start to organize your time, maybe even in the next few weeks, around the activities that vitalize or revitalize you. In a world focused on extrinsic rewards, this book will provide examples of how you can (re)vitalize yourself by focusing on intrinsic rewards.

As a nurse, you are an amazing human. You are no less a nurse because you stop to take care of yourself as well. Our profession continues to be the most trusted profession for a reason. The world trusts nurses to take care of them. Trust, listen, and take care of yourself.

—Dr. Jennifer Mensik

ABOUT THE AUTHORS

Corey S. Pressman, MA, CCFP, CTP, is an instructor in the Integrative Health and Wellness Program at the University of Portland's School of Nursing and Health Innovations. He is also codirector of the Institute for Vital Practice. Corey has an individual coaching practice that assists clients in life direction, emotion regulation, and vitality hygiene. His academic work centers on the practical intersection of integrative wellness, subjective vitality, and organizational change. Corey is also a fellow of Arizona State University's Center for Science and the Imagination, where he participates in innovation workshops and publishes works of speculative fiction. An anthropologist, Corey is also trained in narrative medicine, compassion science, and traumatology. In addition to academic works, he also publishes short stories and poetry. A professional artist, Corey is member/owner of Portland's Blackfish Gallery.

Brylee Kiminski, BS, is a recent graduate from the Integrative Health and Wellness Program at the University of Portland's School of Nursing and Health Innovations. She is also an admitted student in the MPH program at the University of Washington's School of Public Health and currently serves as the public health intern at Portland Refugee Support Group. Brylee's undergraduate research and academic work focused on the intersection between psychological theory, ethics, and higher education, as well as the impacts of COVID-19 on college students. Outside of the classroom, she is a barista at a local coffee roaster, a reader, and a community outreach volunteer.

Dr. Chloé Littzen-Brown, PhD, RN, is an assistant professor of nursing at the University of Portland's School of Nursing and Health Innovations and the codirector of the Institute for Vital Practice. Her research is focused on the work-related well-being of nurses in practice. She currently teaches in both the undergraduate and graduate nursing and integrative health programs, and she mentors students in research focusing on nurse well-being. Chloé's research was inspired by her experience with burnout working as a nurse in practice. She hopes that by learning from and working with nurses in practice, we can collaboratively enhance the places nurses work to promote their well-being.

Positionality of Authors

Name	Pronouns	Key Identities	Salient Assumptions and Biases
Corey S. Pressman	He/Him/His	Educator, coach, artist, writer, scientist, mystic, cultural critic, autonomy advocate, father	Many social structures are designed to thwart individual agency and vitality; a shared ethos and practice of subjective vitality and moral imagination can rectify this.
Brylee Kiminski	She/Her/Hers	White queer woman, learner, equity advocate, caregiver, future public health professional	We have the collective responsibility to utilize our resources and continue finding ways to support the vitality of our teams and communities.
Chloé Littzen-Brown	She/Her/Hers	White cis-hetero woman, settler-colonizer, immigrant, nurse, scientist, philosopher, educator, and advocate	Intermodernist; all nurses have epistemic authority; well-being is a fundamental right for all.

Note: We included our positionality as authors so that you, the reader, can understand how we, the authors, see the world, as well as our potential biases, assumptions, and limitations.

Famous

by Naomi Shihab Nye

The river is famous to the fish.

The loud voice is famous to silence,
which knew it would inherit the earth
before anybody said so.

The cat sleeping on the fence is famous to the birds
watching him from the birdhouse.

The tear is famous, briefly, to the cheek.

The idea you carry close to your bosom
is famous to your bosom.

The boot is famous to the earth,
more famous than the dress shoe,
which is famous only to floors.

The bent photograph is famous to the one who carries it
and not at all famous to the one who is pictured.

I want to be famous to shuffling men
who smile while crossing streets,
sticky children in grocery lines,
famous as the one who smiled back.

I want to be famous in the way a pulley is famous,
or a buttonhole, not because it did anything spectacular,
but because it never forgot what it could do.

(By permission of the author, Naomi Shihab Nye, 2021)

The nurse owes the same duties to self as to others, including the responsibility to promote health and safety, preserve wholeness of character and integrity, maintain competence, and continue personal and professional growth.

—Provision 5 of the Code of Ethics for Nurses

A soul-based workplace asks things of me that I didn't even know I had. It's constantly telling me that I belong to something large in the world.

—David Whyte

—

1.

INTRODUCTION

What is to give light must endure burning.

—Victor Frankl

The more empathically attuned we are, the greater level of neural activation and shared pain we experience—aka empathy's double-edge sword.

—Dr. Mark C. Russel

Lack of resources, lack of staffing, lack of getting all our concerns addressed, things like that. Those are very draining, especially when we're supposed to provide patient care and do a good job. But definitely, all the drama from work and things like that, those don't help. If anything, it just makes the environment more toxic and unbearable, definitely, and at one point, it will start affecting the overall well-being of your mental health and your physical health, even your spiritual health.

—Anonymous nurse

Skilled Compassion

Above all else, nurses are givers. They give care, of course, but they also give their time, their attention, and in a very real sense, a piece of themselves. This gift of one's mind and emotions is at the center of the caregiver's world in the form of empathy and compassion.

Skilled caregiving requires skilled *empathy*, the ability to feel and understand the emotional states of others. Also required is skilled *compassion*, taking action to alleviate suffering. Being empathic and compassionate requires giving yourself to others—to their feelings and to their care.

However, empathy and compassion also contain a bitter irony: Witnessing pain causes pain—something that nurses know well. This is true at the deepest levels; exposure to the suffering of others activates neural pathways associated with first-hand suffering. The very empathy that calls us to action cuts us at the same time. **This is the double-edged sword of compassionate service: To be good at compassion, we must be good at suffering.**

Nurses' challenges don't just arise from the double-edged sword of compassion. The demands of the profession—time commitments, accumulative stress, management, and organizational politics—all contribute to the overwhelm that is a root cause of the profession's high attrition rates and growing mental health challenges (Haddad et al., 2022; Littzen-Brown et al., 2023; NSI Nursing Solutions, 2023). In this broader sense, to be good at nursing is to be good at suffering, to develop the skills to sustain the altruism, optimism, energy, and compassion that first called you to caregiving.

Nursing school trained you in the practice of skilled care. This workbook is about skilled suffering. Recent understandings in neurology, psychology, and compassion science provide solutions to the riddle of the double-edged sword. There are indeed evidence-based methods for supporting compassionate action, gaining energy from this work, and successfully and continually coping with the stresses and strains inherent to caring about and for others.

This workbook is organized by the key elements of skilled compassion. Starting with the foundational abilities of managing *stress* and subjective *vitality*, the workbook progresses through *emotional regulation* and *compassion science* (see Figure 1–1). Each of these elements is a tool in your toolbox to help you wield the double-edged sword of compassionate service and, ultimately, aid in alleviating your suffering.

A Note on Organizations

While *The Double-Edged Sword* focuses on your skills as an individual compassion practitioner, it is important to note that skilled compassion is not just the responsibility of the individual. It is, of course, essential that we as individuals prepare our

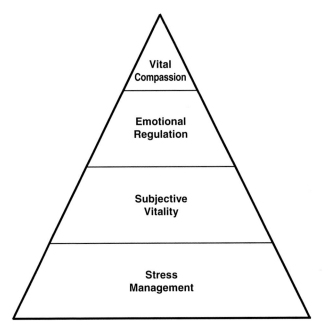

Figure 1–1. Key Components of Skilled Compassion

Activity 1–1: Emotional Acknowledgment

The first step of skilled compassion is to actively acknowledge both edges of the sword.

Let's start by recognizing your *compassion satisfaction*. On the following list of positive feelings, circle those that you commonly experience when providing care. Try using these in a short piece of writing. For example, "When I am caring for patients, I sometimes feel . . ."

◆ Accepting	◆ Comfortable
◆ Active	◆ Courageous
◆ Admiring	◆ Curious
◆ Affectionate	◆ Determined
◆ Amazed	◆ Eager
◆ Amused	◆ Elated
◆ Assertive	◆ Enthusiastic
◆ Attentive	◆ Epiphanic
◆ Brazen	◆ Euphoric
◆ Caring	◆ Excited
◆ Cheerful	◆ Expectant

(continues)

- Fascinated
- Focused
- Friendly
- Grateful
- Happy
- Hopeful
- Humble
- Insightful
- Inspired
- Interested
- Intrigued
- Joyful
- Kind
- Loving
- Mystified
- Nostalgic
- Optimistic
- Passionate
- Proud

- Relaxed
- Satisfied
- Self-caring
- Self-compassionate
- Self-confident
- Self-motivated
- Self-respecting
- Self-understanding
- Sentimental
- Serene
- Strong
- Surprised
- Sympathetic
- Tender
- Thrilled
- Triumphant
- Trusted
- Worthy

Now, let's find the contours of your *compassion stress*. On the list of negative feelings below, circle those that you commonly experience when providing care. Try using these in a short piece of writing. For example, "When I am caring for patients, I sometimes feel . . ."

- Afraid
- Aggressive
- Agitated
- Alienated
- Angry
- Anguished
- Annoyed
- Anxious
- Apathetic
- Apprehensive
- Ashamed

- Baffled
- Bitter
- Bored
- Claustrophobic
- Coercive
- Confused
- Contemptuous
- Cruel
- Demoralized
- Depressed
- Disappointed

- Disgusted
- Disheartened
- Disliked
- Dispirited
- Doubtful
- Frustrated
- Furious
- Grieving
- Guilty
- Helpless
- Hurt
- Impatient
- Insecure
- Irritated
- Isolated
- Jealous
- Lonely
- Mad
- Melancholic
- Miserable
- Moody
- Nauseated
- Neglected
- Nervous
- Numb
- Offended
- Pessimistic
- Powerless
- Rageful
- Regretful
- Rejected
- Reluctant
- Resentful
- Resigned
- Restless
- Sad
- Self-critical
- Self-loathing
- Self-pitying
- Shocked
- Sorrowful
- Spiteful
- Stressed
- Stubborn
- Stuck
- Submissive
- Suffering
- Tense
- Tired
- Troubled
- Uncertain
- Undermined
- Upset
- Weak
- Worried
- Wrathful

Combine all the writing into a single statement about the double-edged sword. This can follow a pattern such as, "When engaging in work as a nurse, I feel both ___positive feelings___ and ___negative feelings___."

This will help you name and acknowledge the emotional complexity of your work. The next exercise is also an effective means of achieving and habituating awareness of your emotional and mental states—an essential first step to engaging with your thoughts and feelings and (re)gaining agency and balance.

> **Activity 1–2: The Morning Pages**
>
> The Morning Pages is a powerful journaling technique propagated by artist, teacher, and writer Julia Cameron in her book *The Artist's Way*. The method is simple. Every day (at least while working through this workbook) find a time, preferably but not necessarily in the morning, and with pen or pencil and paper do the following:
>
> Write down anything that comes to mind—automatically and without pause or long reflection—for two sides of a blank page of notebook paper and one side of a second page.
>
> When you are done, destroy the pages. Rip them out and rip them up; burn them; feed them to the pigs.
>
> Destroying the pages ensures that you are not writing for an audience, not even your future self. This removes any inhibitions from your expression and establishes flow between your head, hand, and heart. Achieving this flow is a central skill for honest and constructive self-exploration. Building a skilled practice of introspection bolsters your ability to better recognize and, ultimately, regulate your internal states.

bodies, psyches, and souls for the good work of giving care, but it is at least equally important that the organizations in which we operate actively support and encourage skilled compassion. With a shared goal of sustainable excellent care, nurses and nurse-hiring institutions must collaborate to design a way of working that centers the essential skills of giving care. Toward this aim, the final section of the workbook addresses institutions, systems, leadership, and change.

References

Haddad, L.M., Annamaraju, P., Toney-Butler, T.J. (2022). Nursing shortage. StatPearls Publishing.

Littzen-Brown, C., Dolan, H., Norton, A., Bethel, C., May, J., & Rainbow, J. (2023). Unbearable suffering while working as a nurse during the COVID-19 pandemic: A qualitative descriptive study. *International Journal of Nursing Studies Advances*, 5, 100127. https://doi.org/10.1016/j.ijnsa.2023.100127

NSI Nursing Solutions. (2023). NSI national health care retention & RNs staffing report. https://www.nsinursingsolutions.com/Documents/Library/NSI_National_Health_Care_Retention_Report.pdf

2.

SUBJECTIVE VITALITY

Entropy Versus Energy

The entire universe is constructed with only a few simple rules, known collectively as the laws of thermodynamics. Chief among these is the law of entropy. Simply stated, entropy is the universal tendency for systems to increase in disorder and randomness over time. Left unsupported, systems leak energy and eventually dissolve into chaos. This is true for molecules, planets, your silverware drawer, and your life. Entropy can be seen as the cause of disorder and malfunction of the systems in which you are embedded—your work, your family, your daily routine, and your mind.

Entropy manifests in our lives as the volatility, uncertainty, confusion, and arbitrariness (collectively known as VUCA) common to everyday life. It also manifests in our emotional reactions to VUCA; left unattended, chronic fear, stress, and sorrow can all work as agents of entropy, draining your systems of their energy and inviting disorder.

The only way to counter entropy, to maintain order and encourage growth, is to add energy into the system. We will call this energy *vitality*, the "positive feeling of being alive and energetic" (Ryan & Frederick, 1997).

Ready and Resilient

There are two kinds of vitality that we can manage: physical and psychological. The sources of physical vitality are well known and include nutrition, exercise, and sleep. While these are indeed very important, this workbook focuses more on *psychological vitality*.

The sources of psychological vitality are less well-known. Also referred to as subjective vitality, psychological vitality is defined as "a sense of energy available to the self" (Ryan & Frederick, 1997). Although it is subjective, this kind of vitality is still measurable and observable. High subjective vitality is a functionally significant indicator of physical and mental health, including immune function, affect, and memory.

If we successfully manage the sources of our psychological vitality, we can assure we have enough energy to counter the entropy always eroding our well-being. In this way, when psychologically vitalized, we are at once *ready* and *resilient*:

- Ready for the inevitable VUCA and suffering that accompanies daily life and that is magnified by being a professional caregiver.
- Resilient enough to get up again should those forces knock you over.

In life, for both work and play, readiness and resilience are required. Subjective vitality is the underlying factor in each.

Regulating Stress

Despite the relative ease and efficacy of the vitality management techniques in this workbook, they will not be accessible or useful to you if you are in a state of stress. Before we learn to work with our vitality, we must first learn to mitigate stress—chronic stress, to be precise.

Stress is a specific set of neurological, psychological, and physiological responses to a perceived threat. As such, stress is a natural and adaptive reflex for all sorts of living creatures, including all mammals, reptiles, and birds. When a threat is perceived, the stress response is automatically engaged by your nervous, endocrine, and immune systems. And when the perceived threat goes away, the stress response turns off. This pattern—threat–stress–relax—is called *acute stress*. Acute stress is good; it saves us from immediate harm and teaches us about danger and safety. It is useful suffering, you might say.

Stress, however, is not always acute. Sometimes we suffer from *chronic stress*. As the name indicates, chronic stress occurs when the stress response does not turn off (see Figure 2–1). Instead, a chronic stress response stays in the on position. This can be attributed to living under chronically threatening conditions or to our unique ability to imagine danger. The human imagination is a gift; it allows us to experience and express worlds beyond the real, to invent and innovate, to tell stories, to connect with others, and to guide our own futures. But, like empathy, it is a double-edged sword. Our imaginations often present danger when there is none or cause us to obsess on anticipated dangers—an agitated and devitalizing state of mind referred to as anticipatory angst. Sound familiar?

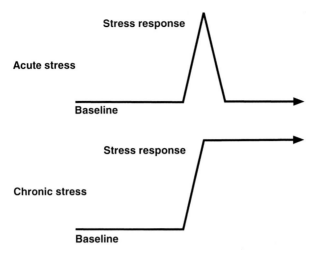

Figure 2–1. Acute Stress Versus Chronic Stress

Chronic stress is not merely a distraction. The physiological toll of being in a prolonged stress state is huge. The following is a list of the common effects of chronic stress. Which combination of these do you typically experience when stressed?

- ◆ Physical effects of chronic stress
  - ▪ Bloating and diarrhea
  - ▪ Frequent illness
  - ▪ Fatigue
  - ▪ Sore muscles
  - ▪ Headaches
  - ▪ Chest pains
  - ▪ Decreased libido
  - ▪ Tinnitus
  - ▪ Insomnia
- ◆ Mental and emotional effects of chronic stress
  - ▪ Depression
  - ▪ Anxiety
  - ▪ Excessive worry
  - ▪ Low affect
  - ▪ Inability to concentrate
  - ▪ Obsessive worrying
  - ▪ Pessimism
  - ▪ Poor judgment
  - ▪ Forgetfulness

Needless to say, it is very difficult to manage your subjective vitality and gain readiness and resilience while stressed out. Learning to regulate your stress will allow you to abbreviate the stress response and regain an ability to think clearly, focus, and act with agency. Only then can you effectively engage in the project of self-vitalization.

Happily, the neurology of stress offers us a simple solution. The stress reflex is governed by the vagus nerve, our longest cranial nerve, which innervates many of your core systems, including the heart, lungs, throat, and the gut. It is also indirectly involved in general muscle tension and the operation of the pelvic floor. The stress reflex recruits all of these systems to get you out of danger.

The vagus nerve is both *afferent* and *efferent*—it both sends signals from the brain down to your body and shuttles signals from the body back up to the brain. So, if you can consciously relax the systems triggered by the stress response, the vagus nerve will inform your brain that all is well and that the stress reflex can be switched off. In other words, you can learn to transform your chronic stress into acute stress.

This can be achieved in a number of ways. Activity 2–1 describes one method that is particularly effective and can be enacted anywhere.

The Sources of Vitality

Psychologists have identified the three universal nutriments of psychological vitality:

◆ Autonomy
◆ Competence
◆ Relatedness

Autonomy refers to the times in which you are engaged in behavior you intrinsically want to do. One is most autonomous when motivated by their values, identities, and interests and least autonomous when motivated by reward, punishment, guilt, and pressure.

As Figure 2–2 indicates, the more autonomous one's motivations, the more vitality they experience. Importantly, the graph indicates that we are most vitalized when motivated by our values and identities. While engaging in our interests and excitements is indeed energizing, these are ultimately more ephemeral and less powerful engagements. We further discuss this later in the chapter.

Competency is a function of appropriate challenge. One gains vitality when engaged in activities that are just challenging enough. Think about a time when achieving your assigned tasks was simply not possible with the resources on hand and how devitalizing that was. It can also be draining to work at a task that is just too easy. But when your work (or play!) is appropriately challenging, vitality flows.

Activity 2–1: The Wet Noodle

This is a progressive relaxation exercise designed to inform your vagus nerve that you are not under physical threat. By doing so, your nervous system will return to the "rest and digest" state and allow you to think clearly and calmly.

Sit comfortably with a softly straightened spine and feet on the floor. You can place your hands on your knees, palms up.

Slowly draw a deep breath and even more slowly exhale through pursed lips. Let's call this a "long exhale" rather than a deep breath; it's the exhale that counts. Do a few of these and notice your heart rate slowing down.

- Start by intentionally relaxing the muscles in your shoulders and your neck. Your head weighs about 10 pounds. Relieve your neck from the duty of having to hold that up anymore. Let your chin fall toward your chest as your muscles relax.

- Now release control of the muscles in your face. You no longer have to hold your cheeks in place. Relax the muscles around your eyes and give a long exhale.

- Wiggle your fingers, move your elbows around a little bit, and let your arms go slack in your lap.

- Now give a long exhale and let your rib cage slump over onto your belly. You no longer need to hold your body up straight. Relax.

- Wiggle your toes and let your knees go where they will.

- Now give a long exhale and then squeeze the muscles in your pelvis as if you're stopping yourself from peeing. Hold this for three seconds. Then release and give a long exhale.

- Slowly open your eyes and raise your head.

Welcome back! Hopefully, you are now calmed and able once again to think clearly and be fully aware of the present. Consider practicing this exercise at least once or twice a day. This will help build the habit of volitionally switching the state of your autonomic nervous system. It also works really well in the moment should a stress episode occur. Of course, it is not always appropriate to stop everything and enact a whole Wet Noodle. In those cases, taking a few long exhales and relaxing your shoulders and pelvis will go a long way toward steering you away from your stress response. This is especially true if you've been practicing your Wet Noodles every day.

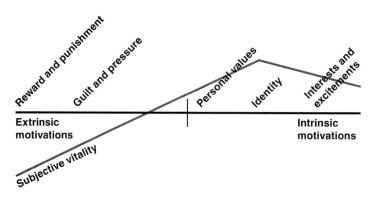

Figure 2–2. Motivation Spectrum

Relatedness occurs when we engage in supportive and meaningful relationships. Vitality from relatedness is experienced when one is connected to others via validating relationships. It's not only relationships that give relatedness but also the feeling of being seen and understood. This is easier for some people to achieve than deep relationships. This may manifest in interpersonal groups such as a work- or play-oriented community. It may also arise in more personal one-on-one relationships with friends and family. Vitalizing relationships validate who we are and elevate our sense of potential.

To these, we can add a fourth important source of subjective vitality that appears to be as universal as autonomy, competency, and relatedness:

Interaction with nature, whether walking in the woods, just going outside, caring for houseplants, or playing with your pets, is associated with elevated vitality as well as a collection of other health benefits (see Activity 2–2).

The ACoRN Test

Remember the sources of vitality easily by employing this simple acronym:

Autonomy, Competency, Relatedness, Nature —> ACoRN

Managing your vitality starts with being aware of—and providing growth conditions for—your ACoRN. To get started, you can audit your current activities, relationships, and commitments using the ACoRN test. The ACoRN test is a simple way to evaluate if something will be vitalizing.

For example, let's say you were asked to pick up an extra shift at work. Your immediate response to this opportunity/request/invitation is likely to be based on a

Activity 2–2: Forest Bathing

Forest bathing, or as it is called in Japanese, *shinrin-yoku*, is the practice of walking in the woods, bathing in the sights, sounds, and smells of the natural environment. Studies indicate that nature-dosing has a demonstrably positive effect on mood, stress regulation, mindfulness, and physiological outcomes, including lower blood pressure as well as measurably lower cortisol levels.

Try this. Find a suitable natural space. This could be a park, a garden, a nature trail, or even an arboretum in a building. Set aside at least 20 minutes to visit this space alone. Once you arrive, do a Wet Noodle and then take the following steps:

- Walk through the space and bring your attention to your senses. What can you smell? What colors, shapes, and textures do you see? What can you hear?

- Notice things you can see but not hear. Notice things you can hear but not see.

- Stand still, close your eyes, and listen to all the sounds you can hear. Try to locate them in space. Make a mental map of the space based on sound alone.

- Now continue your walk leading with your nose. Do the scents change as you move through space? What colors do they smell like?

- When you are done, try another Wet Noodle.

variety of factors, including how you feel, how much time you may have, and even the weather. Employing the ACoRN test, however, will help you factor subjective vitality into the equation.

Let's provide a potential audit of this example:

$$A\uparrow$$

This opportunity is right up my alley; it is well aligned with what I value and is something I truly intrinsically want to do.

$$Co\uparrow$$

This task would indeed be appropriately challenging. I don't think I will be overwhelmed by the requirements and activities. In fact, I believe I stand to learn something from this.

$$R \uparrow$$

The other people on the team all seem really interesting. Also, I look forward to working with people who overlap with my interests so nicely.

$$N \uparrow$$

This event takes place outside, so I will be able to take some outdoor breathing breaks and walk around the grounds a bit, admiring the greenery.

Our audit revealed what appears to be a vitalizing opportunity: $A \uparrow Co \uparrow R \uparrow N \uparrow$. Overall, you are likely to be vitalized, or V+, by deciding to commit to this. In this way, the ACoRN test makes plain the vitality dimension of decision-making, and we cannot begin to center vitality in our lives without a simple and informal way of assessing vitality.

This scenario was decidedly rosy. Of course, many times, maybe even more times than not, the ACoRN test reveals a V– score. Discovering that a behavior will cause you to spend vitality is powerful knowledge. You are now equipped to better budget your psychological energy. Of course, there are many times in life when you will engage in V– situations, either out of duty or desire. That's life. But if you (and the organizations and institutions to which you belong) continue to prioritize subjective vitality, you will have enough vitality to spend on these moments and, potentially, gain from them.

See Activity 2–3 to practice ACoRN testing.

Activity 2–3: ACoRN Testing

Choose an upcoming event or opportunity and evaluate whether it is vitalizing (V+), devitalizing (V–), or somewhere in between (V⁰). You can also try this with an event from your past. Does the event's ACoRN assessment match up to your vitality experience?

Now, think about an upcoming opportunity. Evaluate this using the ACoRN test and see how vitalizing it might be. If it is V–, how might this be redesigned to be more vitalizing? By completing the ACoRN assessment, will you change any of your current or future behaviors when asked to do something?

Your Life Support Mosaic

Life Support

I, Corey Pressman, recently conducted an informal poll of my colleagues in the School of Nursing. The question was simple: What are things you like to do on your own time that are vitalizing? The responses may look familiar to you:

- Cooking
- Singing in the car
- Yoga
- Napping
- Hiking
- Rowing
- Meditation
- Gardening
- Listening to music
- Family time
- Dog time
- Puzzles
- Reading mysteries
- Exercising

These activities are what we may consider common hobbies. However, if our goal is to maximize our vitality, it is fruitful to reframe how we think about these vitalizing activities. Instead of mere hobbies, think of these as your *life support*. Given the importance of vitality for sustained well-being, resilience, and readiness, it makes sense to prioritize activities that energize you. In fact, it is essential. Use Activity 2–4 to determine your life support.

Activity 2–4: Your Life Support

Make a list of the activities that vitalize you. It doesn't matter if you have not engaged in these recently. You can even include things you would like to do but have never done.

Of course, being a nurse precludes doing only the things on your life support list all the time. However, imagine a world in which you purposely structured one or two (or three!) of your life support activities into your day, week, or month. What would that look like? Write it down! You likely can't do them all, and nor do you have to, not all at once, at least. It's best to start small and build up over time.

The Mosaic

To help you decide what life support to structure into your calendar, look at the big picture of how all of your time is spent. To do this, think of your various activities as tiles in a great mosaic that is your daily life. For example, there may be a tile for work, a tile for family time, one for gardening, and so on. In constructing your mosaic, start with the less moveable tiles—things like work and family time. For example, Figure 2–3 shows the central tiles for Meredith, a nurse colleague. Off to the side, she made a tile for each of her various life support vitalizing activities.

This arrangement allows you to see which V+ activity you might choose to incorporate in your life, at least for the next few weeks. After a while, you can reevaluate your mosaic and see if it is working for you. In the case of Meredith, she decided to intentionally integrate cooking and mountain hikes into her weekly routine. Her mosaic now looks like Figure 2–4.

Her choice to include these was based on how readily they could realistically be achieved. Remember, her hikes and cooking are not mere hobbies or things that "would be nice to do." Instead, these activities have been reframed as life support. Without the subjective vitality provided by hiking, she is risking low vitality and, ultimately, burnout. Activity 2–5 guides you in building your mosaic.

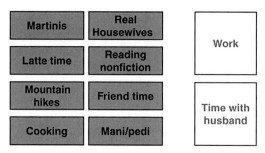

Figure 2–3. Meredith's Vitalizing Activities

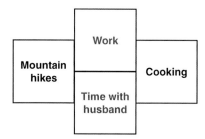

Figure 2–4. Meredith's Vitalizing Activities Mosaic

1. First, place the tiles that cannot move—activities like work and family.
2. Then, use the list from the previous activity and create life support tiles over to the side like in the earlier example.
3. Now, decide which of the life support tiles you can move over into your mosaic for a while.
4. Draw your new mosaic on a piece of paper (or use Post-it notes on paper or the fridge). Keep this somewhere you can see it regularly.

Now that your mosaic is done, you are ready to turn it into action and fold some vitality into your life. How you activate your mosaic is a matter of your personal relationship to structure. Some people need to really make room for their life support by explicitly adding activities to their calendar on specific days and at specific times. For others, it may suffice to be more improvisational and just go with a personal promise to get around to the life support activities. Which approach might work best for you?

Vital Solitude

Solitude is the state of being truly physically alone as well as disengaged from activity that connects you to the outside world for at least 15 minutes. Episodes of *vital solitude* offer an opportunity for resetting, introspection, and vitalization. The practice of vital solitude is an intentional experience, a creation of space to spend authentic time with oneself free of the interference of others and the inevitable public self-awareness that occurs when we interact socially.

Crafting your own practice of solitude will create the conditions for vital reflection, insights, creativity, and self-acceptance. The *vital solitude rituals* (see Activity 2–6) proposed next were designed to pass the ACoRN test by

- Existing as an intrinsic, judgment-free, self-empathic activity (autonomy);
- Enabling the individual to work through potential discomfort with spending time truly alone (competence);
- Creating the conditions for the individual to better explore and understand oneself (relatedness); and
- Being transferable to the outdoors (nature).

Activity 2–6: Vital Solitude Ritual

Begin this practice by getting yourself to a state in which you are truly alone. To do this, disconnect from your screens and devices (with the exception of turning on some music if that is comfortable for you) to avoid distractions. Now, step into comfortable clothing and prepare a warm beverage such as tea. Now that the basics are covered, you can take one of two paths: get seated and cozy or head out on a relaxing, solo walk.

If you choose to sit, prepare to set a 15-minute timer and nestle into a cozy spot. You have a few options of how you can spend this time seated:

- Haiku about you: following the traditional Japanese 5-7-5 syllable structure, release your inner poet.
- Doodle: grab a sheet of paper and writing utensils and sketch to your heart's desire.
- Just think: relinquish all activity and simply sit with your thoughts. As you do, try to be aware of how and where your thoughts are wandering.

If you choose to walk, prepare to set a 15-minute timer and toss on your walking shoes. You have a few options of how you can spend your walk:

- Collect: gather a few random treasures while trekking around (e.g., leaves, stones, or trash to tidy your neighborhood!).
- Color spotting: choose a color and observe your surroundings as you follow your color from place to place.
- Wander: simply roam around your place of choice without a plan or destination.

Designating a time to be alone and do almost nothing can be remarkably challenging. However, you will find that crafting repeatable solitude rituals can provide a reliable dose of clarity, confidence, and vitality.

Purpose Statement

In developing readiness and resilience in the face of challenging and uncertain situations, few things are as useful as possessing a clear *purpose statement* (see Activity 2–7). A good purpose statement summarizes your intrinsic motivations, describes your values and identities, and acts both as a motivator and as a reminder when things get tough. After stress regulation, traumatologists list this clarity of purpose as the most important tool when confronted with overwhelm.

Activity 2–7: Statement of Purpose

1. Make a list of your values. Think of your values as things that you feel are important, central, and essential for a good life. This list of values can help you get started:

   - Abundance
   - Acceptance
   - Authenticity
   - Autonomy
   - Balance
   - Beauty
   - Calmness
   - Caregiving
   - Change
   - Charity
   - Community
   - Compassion
   - Connection
   - Courage
   - Creativity
   - Efficiency
   - Fairness
   - Forgiveness
   - Generosity
   - Goodness
   - Gracefulness
   - Gratitude
   - Grit
   - Harmony
   - Honesty
   - Hope
   - Humility
   - Humor
   - Independence
   - Insightfulness
   - Integrity
   - Joy/Fun
   - Justice
   - Kindness
   - Learning
   - Love
   - Loyalty
   - Openness
   - Peacefulness
   - Self Transcendence

2. Now, list your identities. These can include family identities like sister or father. Also include identities from work, such as nurse, manager, or teacher. Go even deeper and include more generalized and essential identities, such as caregiver, learner, sharer, facilitator, or catalyst. What are the patterns in your life? What is a role you commonly gravitate to in situations? What roles vitalize you most?

3. Begin to craft your statement of purpose based on your responses. Try following this pattern: I am a ___(identity)___ of ___(value)___. Experiment with different words and be playful. You'll know you are on to something when the statement you are crafting begins to excite you. It is not important for your statement to be perfect or beautiful. Don't think of this as something that needs to be clear enough to be shared as is or readily understood by someone else; it only needs to make sense to you.

Your purpose statement is an essential tool capable of orienting you toward your vitality in a few ways:

- Let your purpose statement guide you when deciding whether to commit to a task, opportunities, or activity. As with the ACoRN test, you can use your purpose statement to gauge opportunities as well as make and defend decisions.
- You can also rely on your statement of purpose when deciding *how* to engage in tasks, opportunities, and activities. Your most vital (and vitalizing) contribution to any endeavor is summarized by your statement of purpose. Staying on purpose is a win-win: You receive vitality from your work while your colleagues and patients benefit from your vital contribution.

Remember, vitality is essential for your survival. This isn't self-indulgence. This is self-preservation. This is self-validation.

Activity 2–8 helps you measure your vitality.

To help access a clear statement of purpose, let's return to the motivation spectrum from before (see Figure 2–5).

Your statement of purpose derives from the values and identities portion of the spectrum, where you are intrinsically motivated by your values and identity. This is the reason you went into a caregiving profession such as nursing; it is also the standard by which you can both seek and advocate for your vitality. A clear statement that encapsulates your values and identities provides an essential touchstone when you are making decisions big and small and when things get rough and you need a reminder as to why you are who—and where—you are.

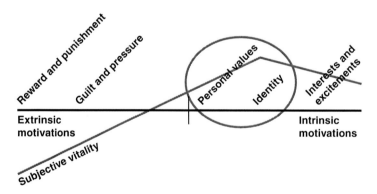

Figure 2–5. The Motivation Spectrum: Purpose Statement

Activity 2–8: The Subjective Vitality Survey

The simple questionnaire in Figure 2–6 is an effective tool for measuring your subjective vitality in the moment. Take the survey now and gain a baseline measurement. As you work on and begin to live via your purpose statement and mosaic, take the survey on occasion. Is your vitality growing?

Determine your scale score by averaging the item scores. Item #2 has to be reverse scored before it is averaged with the other items. Simply subtract your score on item #2 from 8 before averaging the resulting number with your responses on the remaining six items.

State Level Version
Vitality Scale

Please respond to each of the following statements in terms of how you are feeling right now. Indicate how true each statement is for you at this time, using the following scale:

1	2	3	4	5	6	7
Not at all true			Somewhat true			Very true

1. At this moment, I feel alive and vital.
2. I don't feel very energetic right now.
3. Currently I feel so alive I just want to burst.
4. At this time, I have energy and spirit.
5. I am looking forward to each new day.
6. At this moment, I feel alert and awake.
7. I feel energized right now.

Figure 2–6. The Subjective Vitality Survey

Reference

Ryan, R. M., & Frederick, C. (1997). On energy, personality, and health: Subjective vitality as a dynamic reflection of well-being. *Journal of Personality, 65*(3), 529–565. https://doi.org/10.1111/j.1467-6494.1997.tb00326.x

3.

EMOTIONAL REGULATION

Descartes's faith in his assertion 'I think, therefore I am' may be superseded by a more primitive affirmation that is part of the genetic makeup of all mammals: 'I feel, therefore I am.'

—Jaak Panksepp

The Reflex

I was assisting in a morally distressful situation where a child was dying and the patients didn't speak English so they couldn't understand what was going on. We, unfortunately, couldn't get an interpreter in their dialect. All I could focus on was the overwhelming feeling of moral distress for the family, and felt frozen in time.

—Anonymous nurse

In this story, we see a familiar pattern for nurses: Her emotional experience of the situation was immediate. Before they could even think about what to do to help the situation, she had an "overwhelming feeling" about the moral dilemma at hand. This highlights the fact that emotions are immediate. We experience emotions so immediately and subconsciously that emotional responses may be better described as emotional reflexes. Just like other reflexes such as the gag reflex, the startle reflex, and the patellar reflex, emotional reactions to external (and internal) stimuli are automatic and mostly out of our control. But unlike the cough reflex, emotions inform our mood, mind, and behavior. Our emotions have a profound effect on how we experience and interact with the world. It is therefore essential to have a skilled working relationship with your emotional responses.

Neurologists have identified seven basic emotional states, or *core affects* (see Table 3–2), experienced by all mammals:

- JOY (pleasure)
- FEAR (anxiety)
- RAGE (anger)
- LUST (sexual excitement)
- DISGUST (revulsion)
- GRIEF (sadness)
- EXCITEMENT (eagerness).

Other, more complex emotions, like the many types of love, are subtle secondary combinations of and reactions to these core affects. For example, what we call romantic love is a blend of lust, excitement, and joy.

Human cultures assign a variety of words for these basic mammalian emotions. We may consider these labels as *feelings*—cultural-bound interpretations of the core emotions (see Table 3–1).

Emotions Are Informational

> *Eventually the baby died, and we did get an interpreter to talk with the family. It was just so sad and unnecessarily traumatic for everyone involved. I still think about it today, including how I reacted and felt in those moments; I don't think I ever really processed it.*
>
> —Anonymous nurse

This story points out an important dynamic—many times our emotional reflex results in immediate action. But these *emotional actions* are often less than helpful. Our emotions are neurological reflexes that evolved to inform us about the environment. As such, they can be very useful and, in turn, motivational. However, as a human being equipped with years of experience, training, and priorities aside from survival and reproduction, you should develop the skill of getting beyond the reflex and

Table 3-1. Emotions Versus Feelings

Emotions	Feelings
Reflexes that occur following internal or external stimuli	Words that are culturally correlated and assigned to emotions
Prompted before associated with feelings	Labeled as a result of emotional reflexes
Physiological reflexes	Culturally correlated and assigned language
Able to be noticed through bodily and physiological response	Able to be hidden

Table 3-2. Core Affects and Related Feelings

Core Affects	Associated Feelings
Joy	Elation, happiness, content, delight, glee, bliss, euphoria, satisfaction
Fear	Anxiety, apprehension, uneasiness, worry, distress, dread, shock, terror, panic, fright
Rage	Anger, fury, hostility, bitterness, hatred, disgust, resentment, sadness, frustration, aggravation, agitation
Lust	Arousal, excitement, attraction, admiration, desire, passion
Disgust	Revulsion, horror, nausea, loathing, distaste, repugnance
Grief	Sadness, isolation, powerlessness, shame, hurt, despair, vulnerability, sorrow, hopelessness, brokenheartedness, detachment
Excitement	Enthusiasm, exhilaration, engagement, creativity, passion, anticipation

accessing more of your mind. Of course, emotions cannot be ignored, nor should they be disregarded (if that were even possible). Instead, we can learn to treat our emotions as *information* rather than as *instructions*.

Emotional regulation can be defined as the skill of listening to our emotions, then acting from our whole minds. When in your whole mind, you are in a posture that psychologist Richard Schwartz summarizes with the Seven Cs:

- ◆ Calm
- ◆ Curious
- ◆ Connected
- ◆ Compassionate
- ◆ Confident
- ◆ Courageous
- ◆ Clear

Emotional regulation allows you to ally with your emotions, learn from them, then meet the world with your whole mind. This requires two central skills as you reflect on how you feel in the moment:

- Recognizing your emotional state
- Accepting your emotional state

Recognizing Your Emotional State

Technically, each core affect is a discrete and identifiable neurological-endocrinological event. We don't just feel emotions in our brains; each is associated with various body sensations correlated with the unique neurological and hormonal fingerprint of that emotion. For example, I feel fear in my gut—a sort of churning right at my solar plexus. The first step of emotional regulation is becoming aware of (see Activity 3–1)—and naming (see Activity 3–2)—which core affect you are experiencing. This is facilitated by becoming familiar with how each of your emotions feel in your body.

Emotional Reflex Diary

Date: _____
Core Affect(s): _____
Feelings: _____
_____

Sensations: Where in your body do you experience this? Indicate where and what the sensations are on the below figure:

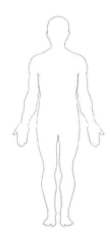

Insights: What are some insights into what triggered this emotional reflex? What can be learned from this?

_____

_____

_____

_____

_____

Activity 3–1: Map Your Emotions
Using the human figures in Figure 3–1, indicate where and how you generally feel each of the core affects.

Activity 3–2: Name Your Emotions
Emotional skill requires the ability to recognize your emotions as they arise. Gaining familiarity with your emotional reflexes will help you manage them. Since they are mostly automatic, you cannot stop your emotions from occurring, nor do we want that. Whether appetitive or aversive, our emotions are part of the rich fabric of our subjective reality, and they inform us about what we seek and what brings us vitality. The following exercise will help you build the habit of being aware of your emotional reflexes—the first step in making them informative.

Over the course of the next few days, be aware of your emotional reflexes. Ask yourself, "What am I feeling right now? Where am I feeling it in my body?" Using Table 3–2 on page 25, name and locate the emotions you experienced and the circumstances in which you experienced them.

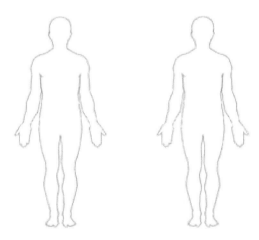

Figure 3–1. Map Your Emotions

Accepting Your Emotional State

> *As a nurse, it's really difficult when terrible things are happening in front of you and you have to hold back your emotions—your humanness. To want to cry when someone dies and you can't, is heavy. When you hold onto that emotion rather than letting it be in the moment with the people they belong with, it builds up.*
>
> —Anonymous nurse

This story illustrates an important dynamic. Aversive emotions like fear, anger, and grief do not feel good. Also, we may have learned as children that certain emotional reflexes are wrong or inappropriate—don't cry; don't be scared; anger is bad; joy is inappropriate. Understandably, we often cope with uncomfortable or forbidden emotions with various avoidance strategies. Saying no to our emotions, however, interrupts them and prevents the reflex from completing its mission: to inform you. Depending on the reason and strategy, your avoided emotions are at the root of some familiar emotional imbalances.

Avoidance Versus Inquiry

A common strategy for coping with emotions we don't want to feel is to avoid them—just sweep them under the rug and carry on. This is a natural reaction to discomfort; it arises from a sincere and healthy desire to protect ourselves. Indeed, there are many times it would be unwise to let your emotions ride. However, prolonged avoidance of emotions can produce some debilitating results:

- **Anxiety/panic**: an acute stress response caused by fearing and avoiding emotional reflexes.
- **Shame**: a painful belief that we are somehow *bad at being people* for having certain emotions. Shame triggers the kind of self-talk that constitutes what psychologists call our *core negative image*. While experiencing shame, you might tell yourself,
  - I am not good enough.
  - I am a failure.
  - I am not lovable.
  - I am stupid.
- **Depression**: some forms of depression result from a desire to defend ourselves from our emotions. Dimming your ability to feel your feelings defends you from feeling how you don't want to feel. The way

the brain works, however, does not allow you to depress a single emotion. It must instead depress your emotionality entirely, greatly impeding your access to the richness of life, your whole mind, and the sources of vitality.

Shame, anxiety, depression—all of these may result from saying no to our emotional reflexes. If, however, we can gain the skill of saying yes and being present with our feelings, we can ask them questions so that we can learn from them and return to the calm, curious, connected, compassionate, confident, courageous, and clear state of working with your whole mind.

For building core emotional strength and presence, see Activities 3–3 and 3–4.

Activity 3–3: Building Core Emotional Strength

This activity builds on the previous two. Just like last time, fill out the emotional reflex sheet while reflecting on a recent emotional experience. This time, choose a negative emotion, preferably one you are presently experiencing or have recently experienced. After naming the emotion, hold onto it. Performing this exercise repeatedly is like going to an emotional reflex gym; it will build your core emotional strength and instill in you the healthy habit of self-empathy.

- Do a Wet Noodle (see Chapter 2) and really feel the emotion in your body. Now, ask yourself these questions:

  - Which of the core affects am I experiencing?
  - What triggered or activated these emotions?
  - Why did these emotions activate when they did?
  - What is this emotional reflex trying to inform me about my environment?

- Write the answers to these questions in the form.

Activity 3–4: Presence

Successful emotional inquiry requires a particular ability—the skill of being present. *Presence*, or as it is sometimes called, mindfulness, is the art of being aware of your present moment and place as opposed to being in a distracted frame of mind, caught up in automatic behaviors, reactions to emotional reflexes, and anticipatory angst.

Becoming present is the purpose of the Wet Noodle exercise discussed in Chapter 2, which is a great tool for accessing mindfulness right away. To help

(continues)

build the habit of presence in the long term, try the following poetic exercise, which takes its form from a poem jotted in the margins of a Bible by an anonymous 9th century Irish monk. It is beautiful (and quite modern) in its simplicity. It is a poem that grows out of paying attention to the natural world.

I Have News
by Anonymous, 9th century

I have news for you:
The stag bells, winter snows, summer has gone

Wind high and cold, the sun low, short its course
The sea running high.

Deep red the bracken; its shape is lost;
The wild goose has raised its accustomed cry,

cold has seized the birds' wings;
season of ice, this is my news.

Try writing an "I Have News" poem of your own. Your poem will describe your immediate environs, whether it's your backyard, your kitchen, or the hospital floor you are rounding on. Start your poem with "I have news..." and finish with "this is my news."

Here is an example from a nurse colleague, Jessica Del Haro:

I have news for you:

The snow has melted only for rain and stormy skies to return;
and for the briefest moment of sunshine to steal the show

I cannot see it, but I can hear drops tip tap against the window
Resting almost comfortably in the seat, cozied up against the wall, the melody of the music almost drowns out my surroundings . . .

Still the rustlings around me manage to find their way into my ears, making themselves known
Despite that, I find my solitude amongst the dim lighting and peacefulness of those hard at work

My eyes threaten to close, in their attempt to gain some needed sleep, but I stay alert for the moment I hear the trill of my phone

Until that moment comes,
this is my news.

A Path to Vitality

You are encouraged to engage in these exercises with some regularity, at least in the short term. This will allow you to build a habit of emotional acceptance and inquiry—a *prepared reflex* with which to experience and learn from your emotional reflex. A healthy habit of emotional regulation allows you to gain a sort of emotional autonomy associated with your whole mind:

- Access a calm, curious, connected, compassionate, confident, courageous, and clear state.
- Learn from your emotional reflexes.
- Act from informed decision, rather than emotional reaction.
- Access the vitality that one gains from autonomy, competency, and relatedness.

Emotions are notoriously difficult to manage. While the exercises and information in this section may be simple, the actual practice of proactive emotional regulation is by no means easy. Sometimes you will succeed and gain access to your best self. Other times, you will not succeed and your emotions will get the best of you. Merely having tried is a sign of your presence in your own life, an indication that you are self-aware and acting on purpose. For this, you—as much as your patients, your friends, and your children—deserve your compassion.

4.

VITAL COMPASSION

Caregiving professionals are professional compassionists. Recent understandings about the biology, psychology, and sociology of compassion have greatly expanded our knowledge of both its perils and its many benefits. The nascent biopsychosocial field of *compassion science* indicates a set of skills for a vital practice of compassion. This section defines *skilled compassion* and provides some activities to help you build a personal compassion practice that is sustainable, vitalizing, and resilient.

Empathy and Compassion

The terms "empathy" and "compassion" are sometimes used interchangeably. However, there are some significant distinctions between them:

- *Empathy* is the ability to both feel and understand the emotional states of others.
  - *Affective empathy*: Feeling others' emotional states is called affective empathy. Affective empathy occurs in the brain much the same way as our emotional reflexes do. Governed by special mirror neurons, affective empathy is a reflex that occurs when we witness the emotions of another. Some people are born with high affective empathy. As we will see, this can be a sort of superpower; it can also be a super-stressor. Given the neurological workings of affective empathy, it is not really a skill that can be learned. Rather, it is a trait some of us have in varying amounts.
  - *Cognitive empathy*: Cognitive empathy involves understanding others' emotions. It is an intellectual ability to discern the emotional state of those you encounter. Empathic accuracy is the

skill of the cognitive empath. Unlike the trait of affective empathy, this skill can be taught and trained.

- *Compassion* is the desire and act of alleviating suffering. *Vital compassion* is the sustained practice of compassionate action that is vitalizing for the practitioner. In the caregiving professions, vital leaders are engaged in the charismatic project of creating the conditions for vital compassion.

There are a few important distinctions to recognize. Compassion, unlike empathy, is centered only on suffering and its alleviation. Empathy is about all emotions. Also, whereas empathy involves emotions and intellect, compassion is all about motivation and behavior. One acts compassionately after being informed by their empathy. Like affective empathy, some folks seem to be born natural compassionists; they cannot experience or comprehend the suffering of others without wanting to help. But like cognitive empathy, compassion can also be taught and trained. In fact, skilled and sustainable compassion *requires* a certain amount of training, which involves our emotions, our intellect, and our behavior (Table 4–1).

Table 4–1. Empathy and Compassion

	Involves	Trait or trained
Affective empathy	Emotions	Trait
Cognitive empathy	Intellect	Trait and trained
Compassion	Emotions, intellect, and behavior	Trait and trained

Brief and Valuable

Character cannot be developed in ease and quiet. Only through experience of trial and suffering can the soul be strengthened, vision cleared, ambition inspired, and success achieved.

—Helen Keller

When engaging in compassion, it is useful to set a clear boundary around what "alleviation of suffering" means. Compassion can include a variety of impulses and actions, such as

- Soothing immediate pain and discomfort,
- Addressing the root causes of pain and discomfort, and
- Helping to prevent the conditions that cause pain and discomfort.

Notice that this list does not include the complete eradication of all pain and discomfort. Suffering is not just an unavoidable fact of life; it is often the path to gaining actionable wisdom. We should not wish away the ability to feel pain—how, then, would we know that hot surfaces and sharp edges are dangerous? Psychologists, philosophers, and theologians alike all agree that suffering serves our knowledge and wisdom, informs our cognitive empathy, and shapes our lives. In fact, for many of us, it was our own wounds that called us to become caregivers.

If pain, suffering, and discomfort are all informative, essential, and ubiquitous, how do we justify our life's work as compassionists dedicated to the alleviation of suffering? The answer lies in how we define alleviation. A compassionate caregiver works with suffering in order to

- Decrease its duration
- Increase its value

The loving kindness of the active compassionist is centered on the wish for suffering to be *brief* and *valuable*.

See Activity 4–1 for compassion meditation and Activity 4–2 for self-compassion practice.

Compassion Satisfaction, Burnout, and Compassion Fatigue

Being a compassionist requires you to use your empathy as a guide and engage with those who are suffering in order to alleviate their pain. When you are engaging in sustainable, vitalizing compassion, you get to experience one of the greatest joys in life: *compassion satisfaction*. Compassion satisfaction is defined as the joy and dose of vitality one receives from engaging in a compassionate act. We are so wired for compassion satisfaction that we can experience feelings of moral elevation simply from observing compassionate acts.

But if we have such a propensity for compassion satisfaction, why are the caregiving professions so closely associated with burnout, negative feelings, and total exhaustion? What is so dangerous about working with others to make their suffering brief and valuable? As noted previously, much of this dynamic begins with the organizations and systems in which caregivers operate. If these systems do not create the conditions for caregiver vitality and do not support emotional regulation, then they

Activity 4–1: Compassion Meditation

Like any form of exercise, meditation is not easy. However, just like with physical exercise, there are both short- and long-term benefits and it gets easier with practice. In this way, think of meditation as a way of training your mind. In this case, we are training our mind to (a) react to the suffering of others with compassion and (b) define that compassion as an attempt to make suffering brief and valuable. This meditation is based on the "Loving Kindness Meditation" used in the applied compassion training offered by The Center for Compassion and Altruism Research and Education at Stanford University.

Welcome.

Take a deep breath in through your nose . . . and release it, slowly and controlled from your mouth.

Make yourself comfortable. Shaking loose any tension, close your eyes if that makes you comfortable. Take another deep breath here, settling in. Allow yourself to sink into the surface you're resting on and take one more deep breath— picture yourself breathing in bright light and breathing out a sensation of love.

Imagine yourself looking up at a wide flight of colorful stairs, leading to a room filled with a bright yet warm light and the love you are worthy of feeling.

Step onto the first step, allowing a bit of the color and light to rise up through you. Repeat these statements:

- ◆ *I carry strength and resilience with me.*
- ◆ *Abundance and love flow over me.*

Repeat this three times.

Take another step, allowing more color and warmth to radiate through you. Repeat the following statements:

- ◆ *I am worthy of this abundance and love.*
- ◆ *Happiness flows freely from me.*

Repeat three times.

Step onto another colorful step, letting it absorb into your body, along with the warmth and light. Repeat after me:

- *I deserve tenderness and compassion from myself.*
- *I am authentic toward myself and the world around me.*

Repeat three times.

Take another step toward the light, feeling it start to warm your skin. Repeat these statements:

- *I am a healer of myself and others.*
- *I wish wellness and love onto myself and those around me.*

Repeat three times.

You are stepping up and through the doorway now. Soak in the color and feel the warmth and light deep in your bones. Picture yourself surrounded by those you love and those who love you. Envision them telling you,

- *I wish you health and vitality.*
- *I wish you love and compassion.*
- *I wish for your suffering to be brief and valuable.*

Repeat these statements back to them, reciprocating that love.

Repeat these statements unto yourself, directing the abundance and love within.

Soaking in this love, warmth, and light, bring your awareness back toward your physical body. Take three deep breaths here:

- *Deep breath in . . . and out . . .*
- *Inhale . . . and exhale . . .*
- *One more breath in . . . and out . . .*

Gently move your fingers and toes, and when you're ready, open your eyes.

Engage in this meditation once every few days. Notice how it gets easier to concentrate. Also notice how your practice of compassion grows more vitalizing.

Activity 4–2: Self-Compassion Practice

This is an opportunity to apply the tools of sustainable compassion to your own suffering. Just like enacting compassion for others, self-compassion requires empathy, intent, and action.

When you notice you are suffering from negative emotions or stress, do a Wet Noodle as you conduct these four reflections:

- Recognize and name the suffering: *"I am angry and stressed out because . . ."*
- Regard your suffering self with the warmth and kindness that you would a friend or patient. Try using your own name when doing this. Offer some kind words to yourself.
- Ask yourself how we might abbreviate this suffering. Sometimes this is *not* doing something—not acting from our emotions, not hiding, not drinking, and so on.
- Reflect on what this suffering can teach you: How can you find value, growth, and wisdom from this?

Remember that all people suffer sometimes and that you are not at all alone in this. May our suffering be brief and valuable.

Try being explicit about these four reflections whenever you can. Doing this exercise will help build the habit of compassionate self-reflection and just might help you find a way to transform your pain into vitality.

are inadvertently designed to expose caregivers to compassion's shadows: *compassion stress* and *compassion fatigue.*

Compassion stress occurs when your compassionate action results in a chronic stress response. Technically, the stress response in the moment is likely the result of an accumulation of stressors from both your private and professional worlds. But being cut by the double-edged sword of empathy is often what pushes us over the edge. Compassion stress is attributed to

- Chronic workplace-related stressors
- Difficulty regulating emotions, especially those emotions we feel as a result of being empathic caregivers in the presence of others' pain— something called *vicarious trauma.*

Institutional stress and vicarious trauma constitute a daily dose of suffering that nurses must manage. The institutional dimension will be addressed in Chapter 5.

This workbook has hopefully provided the perspectives and methods for gaining the vitality required to make your suffering brief and valuable.

Technically, compassion fatigue is a form of what psychologists call a *stress injury*. It is a syndrome, a noxious mixture of chronic stress, depression, and low vitality. Common symptoms of compassion fatigue include the following:

◆ Feeling exhausted physically and psychologically
◆ Feeling helpless, hopeless, or powerless
◆ Feeling irritable, angry, sad, or numb
◆ A sense of being detached or having decreased pleasure in activities
◆ Ruminating about the suffering of others and feeling anger toward the events or people causing the suffering
◆ Blaming yourself and having thoughts of not having done enough to help the people who are suffering
◆ A decreased sense of personal and professional accomplishment
◆ A change in your worldview or spirituality
◆ Physical symptoms, including sleep and appetite disturbances, nausea, and dizziness

Treatment of compassion fatigue often requires psychological counseling and lifestyle changes, including initiating the practices contained in this workbook. The severe condition of compassion fatigue arises from a confluence of a few factors:

◆ Chronic stress
◆ Difficulty regulating emotions, especially those emotions we feel as a result of being empathic caregivers in the presence of others' pain—something called *vicarious trauma*
◆ Burnout

Burnout is a widely used concept that often refers to some form of demotivation or exhaustion caused by chronically challenging circumstances. In this context, we will employ a definition of burnout informed by our concessions of vitality and ACoRN and by the work of traumatologist Eric Gentry: Burnout is the severe vitality depletion that occurs when the perceived demands on us outweigh our perceived resources.

Taken all together, the dynamic of compassion satisfaction and compassion fatigue can be summarized as shown in Figure 4–1. The A portion of the graph depicts the place we all want to be. Here, we are experiencing compassion satisfaction, high vitality, and positive affect. In short, this is when we are in the groove, when we are experiencing flow. In these times, high vitality bolsters your skilled compassion, presence, and emotional core strength. Here, we are ready to meet and benefit from

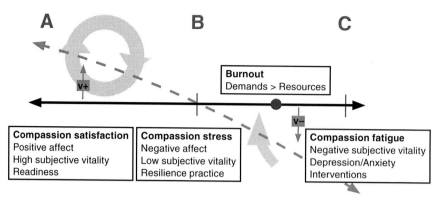

Figure 4-1. The Vital Practitioner Framework

the hardships of our work. The exercises in this workbook are designed to help get you in the groove and keep you in the groove longer.

But of course, we cannot always be in the groove. Life is hard: unexpected events occur, stresses mount, vitality leaks, and things get hard at work and at home. As our vitality depletes, we may begin to feel the destructive power of the double-edged sword. What was once empathic accuracy devolves into empathic distress as our compassionate actions expose us to more and more suffering—suffering we no longer have the vitality, emotional core strength, or presence to handle. This is when we may enter section B of the graph and when we begin to feel the burn. This is when compassion satisfaction mutates into compassion stress. These are the times when lessons learned from the exercises in this workbook can really come in handy.

The information and exercises in this workbook can provide you with the self-awareness and specific skills required to recognize and mitigate the conditions that lead to compassion stress. Switching off stress, safeguarding vitality, regulating emotions, and achieving presence are essential skills to slowing the approach to compassion stress and steering back to compassion satisfaction.

However, as stated earlier (and returned to in the next chapter), this is not only the responsibility of the individual. The organizations and systems in which we work also need to prioritize these skills and create the conditions for compassion satisfaction. All too often, this is not the case. Systems insensitive to compassion stress are at risk of encouraging burnout, and the vitality dive from burnout sets us up for entering section C of the graph—the very serious situation of compassion fatigue.

The Burnout System

You can see from its definition that incidences of burnout explicitly involve perceived demands on our time and attention often made by managers, colleagues, or patients—

demands imposed by "the system." The management and design of systemic demands and nurse resources play a big part in crafting a vital practice of nursing. Left unchecked, the stress injury of compassion fatigue can lead to a variety of mental and physical ailments, including obsessive compulsive disorder, suicidal ideation, clinical depression, digestive issues, immunity issues, and cardiovascular issues. We know this sounds serious, and it is. We know it seems unfair that compassionism should have such a dark shadow. It is. However, by enacting the practices set out in this workbook, you can be ready for it and resilient in face of it. We can also partner with our institutions to design a workplace that promotes vitality over fatigue.

5.

VITAL ORGANIZATIONS

You know that the antidote to exhaustion is not necessarily rest?
. . . The antidote to exhaustion is wholeheartedness.

—David Whyte

The whole workbook up to this point is designed to enable you to approach caregiving and compassion as a *vital practitioner.* The vital practitioner engages in work and life by centering, exchanging, and enhancing their subjective vitality. It is at least equally important that the organizations in which we operate actively support and encourage skilled compassion. And this requires leadership.

Vital Leadership and Vitality Pitfalls

Vital leadership is effective when it achieves increased and maintained individual subjective vitality. It accomplishes this by creating the conditions for followers to acquire the abilities, confidence, and intrinsic motivations to achieve shared charismatic goals. Leaders should prioritize the subjective vitality of their followers by managing and designing work that avoids the two most common vitality pitfalls: the No-Go Zone and the Undermining Effect. These can best be described by consulting Figure 5–1.

In Figure 5–1, the *x*-axis denotes the familiar motivation spectrum from extrinsic to intrinsic motivation. The *y*-axis describes how much structure the work environment provides for a specific task, project, or undertaking. The top of the *y*-axis connotes a highly structured environment with lots of rules, methods, instructions, deadlines, and spreadsheets. At the bottom of the *y*-axis, we find a highly unstructured context

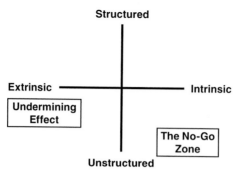

Figure 5–1. The No-Go Zone and the Undermining Effect

with little to no organization or instructions. Notice that the first pitfall, the No-Go Zone, sits in that uncomfortable place when someone is keenly intrinsically motivated to perform a task but has inadequate structure to succeed or even get started. The subsequent frustration and confusion of inhabiting the No-Go Zone can be very devitalizing. We call this the No-Go Zone because when you enter this region, you don't *go*—it is difficult to act without enough structure. It is also called the No-Go Zone because you don't want you or your followers to *go* there, at least not for long.

The second pitfall, the Undermining Effect, is situated on the extrinsic side of the spectrum and doesn't involve structure per se. You inhabit this space when extrinsic motivations, rewards, or demands are offered for something you are already intrinsically motivated to do. This undermining experience is directly associated with decreased vitality.

As leaders, it is our responsibility to design a work environment that avoids opportunities for our followers to end up encountering these pitfalls (see Activity 5–1).

The Sweet Spot

As leaders, it is our job to create the conditions for our followers to better understand the source of their vitality and provide the context, encouragement, and resources for vitality maintenance. Depending on the individual, this sweet spot can fall anywhere outside of the No-Go Zone and Undermining Effect region, as shown in Figure 5–2.

You'll notice variations in people's sweet spots and places from which they derive vitality (see Figure 5–3). Followers suffer when they are not in their vitality sweet spot; learning where they are most vitalized and designing a workplace where they can work within their sweet spot is the first step to making their suffering brief and valuable—the epitome of compassionate leadership. See Activity 5–2.

Activity 5–1: Pitfall Reflection

Now that you are aware of the Undermining Effect and the No-Go Zone, think back on your experiences with these pitfalls. The following reflection exercise can be done alone or with a colleague or two. If you are working alone, write out your responses (you can try destroying them afterward as with the Morning Pages). If you are completing this exercise with a colleague, use the following as discussion prompts:

- First, get comfortable and do a Wet Noodle exercise.
- Next, reflect on any time in your private or work life in which you found yourself in the No-Go Zone or suffering the Undermining Effect. Describe what happened.
- Then, see if you can recall instances when you might have inadvertently guided followers to one of these pitfalls. How did it happen? What might you do differently?

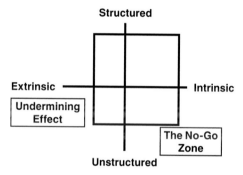

Figure 5–2. The Sweet Spot

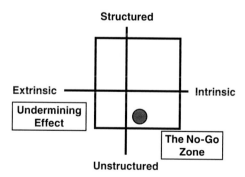

Figure 5–3. Where is Your Sweet Spot?

Vital Leadership Skills

Designing work that centers individual vitality requires leaders with a variety of skills in any day and age. However, in our rapidly evolving times, leaders have the opportunity to facilitate systems that enable followers to thrive in the presence of liminality, volatility, and uncertainty. This sort of *liminal leadership* leverages uncertainty and rapid change as opportunities for transformational growth by activating and propagating readiness and resilience. This is how we realize intentional change amidst the chaos.

To accomplish this, vital leaders must engage in specific personal skill building and leadership techniques. Fortunately, the skills required are those outlined in this workbook:

- Stress mitigation
- Vitality regulation
- Emotional regulation
- Practical compassion

Research indicates that, in addition to practicing these skills, effective change leaders engage with followers in a way that is adaptive, directed, and relational. Each of these dimensions recruits different skills, listed in Table 5–1.

Table 5–1. Vital Leadership Skills

Dimension	Explanation	Skills
Adaptive	Ability to adapt to followers, organizational needs, and shifting circumstances	Resilience Comfort with uncertainty Self-awareness
Directive	Creating and propagating charismatic goals that motivate and vitalize followers	Sense-making Consensus building Storytelling
Relational	Nurturing authentic relationships with followers and supporting their growth with compassion	Active listening Relationship management Compassion

Activities 5–3 and 5–4 are designed to help you develop the essential skill of active listening and self-awareness.

Activity 5–3: Active Listening

Practice the six techniques of active listening:

- Pay attention: give the speaker your full attention by looking at them directly and noticing their body language.
- Withhold judgment: be open to hearing new ideas and perspectives while holding back any criticisms or interruptions.
- Reflect: do not assume you know what the speaker is trying to say, but instead, try paraphrasing their points to be sure you understand what they mean.
- Clarify: ask questions to clear up any doubt or confusion about what the speaker is trying to say (e.g., "Will you tell me about . . . ?" or "Will you further explain . . . ?").
- Summarize: Restate the speaker's key points to demonstrate your understanding of what they are telling you.
- Share: here is where you can introduce your ideas or suggestions (if the speaker is willing to hear them) to work together to move forward toward the problem.

For this exercise,

- Break into pairs or groups and take turns sharing a story or scenario relevant to your workplace, exercising the active listening techniques when it is your turn as listener.

(continues)

- Debrief afterward to better understand how it felt being the speaker in a situation with an active listener and how it felt to practice active listening.
- Together, share the combined outcomes or even challenges with active listening that could be improved.

Activity 5–4: Personality Challenges

Personality tests like the Myers–Briggs and the Enneagram can be surprisingly accurate in describing our various strengths and proclivities. Much can be gained, however, by focusing on the personal challenges these tests reveal.

For example, according to the personality test at 16personalities.com, I am an Extraverted, Intuitive, Feeling, and Prospecting (ENFP) personality type. And while their detailed description of my various personality tendencies is accurate, so is the list of weaknesses ENFPs possess: people-pleasing, unfocused, disorganized, overly accommodating, overly optimistic, and restless. So true!

Having these weaknesses so explicitly delineated offers a useful opportunity, one that this exercise will help you leverage. You may successfully do this exercise alone; however, it is powerful (and fun!) to collaborate with a friend or colleague:

- Go to 16personalities.com or a similar personality test and take the test.
- Review the challenges or weaknesses associated with your personality type and list the ones that seem the most accurate. Of these, pick one in particular that you would like to work on and that seems in your comfort zone to do so in the short term.
- Strategize on how you (or your friend or colleague) might consciously work on this trait. For example, as an ENFP, I am notoriously disorganized. Knowing this, I can work with a colleague who is good at organization and devise some organizational strategies and habits.

Toward a Vital Future

Ultimately, leaders have the opportunity (and responsibility) to transform their workplaces into *vital organizations*. These are systems designed to center subjective vitality and compassionate action while bringing people together to achieve shared goals. Organizations, societies, and cultures are composed primarily of people. And while their ways and means may seem set in stone, ultimately they can be as flexible as the human mind and as strong as our hearts. As vital practitioners and leaders, we can collaborate to craft ways of being and working that allow us to access and administer vital compassion.

A.

REFERENCES AND RECOMMENDED READINGS FOR VITAL PRACTICE

The foundation of this workbook rests on existing theories, research, and evidence-based practices spanning several academic disciplines and categories; these categories and some respective sources can be found here. These references and recommended readings are not intended as an exhaustive list of the literature; instead, this serves as a collection of relevant resources informing on the content in this workbook.

Self-Determination Theory

Busque-Carrier, M., Ratelle, C. F., & Le Corff, Y. (2022). Work values and job satisfaction: The mediating role of basic psychological needs at work. *Journal of Career Development*, *49*(6), 1386–1401. https://doi.org/10.1177/08948453211043878

Deci, E. L., Olafsen, A. H., & Ryan, R. M. (2017). Self-determination theory in work organizations: The state of a science. *Annual Reviews*, *4*, 19–43. https://doi.org/10.1146/annurev-orgpsych-032516-113108

Ryan, W. S., & Ryan, R. M. (2019). Toward a social psychology of authenticity: Exploring within-person variation in autonomy, congruence, and genuineness using self-determination theory. *Review of General Psychology*, *23*(1), 99–112. https://doi.org/10.1037/gpr0000162

Weinstein, N., Przybylski, A. K., & Ryan, R. M. (2009). Can nature make us more caring? Effects of immersion in nature on intrinsic aspirations and generosity. *Personality and Social Psychology Bulletin*, *35*(10), 1315–1329. https://doi.org/10.1177/0146167209341649

Compassion Fatigue

Figley, C. R. (1995). Compassion fatigue: Toward a new understanding of the costs of caring. In B. H. Stamm (Ed.), *Secondary traumatic stress: Self-care issues for clinicians, researchers, and educators* (pp. 3–28). The Sidran Press.

Gentry, J. E., & Dietz, J. J. (2020). *Forward-facing professional resilience: Prevention and resolution of burnout, toxic stress and compassion fatigue.* Outskirts Press.

Russell, M., & Brickell, M. (2015). The "double-edge sword" of human empathy: A unifying neurobehavioral theory of compassion stress injury. *Social Sciences, 4*(4), 1087–1117. https://doi.org/10.3390/socsci4041087

Stress

Porges, S. W. (2009). The polyvagal theory: New insights into adaptive reactions of the autonomic nervous system. *Cleveland Clinic Journal of Medicine, 76*(4, Suppl. 2), S86–S90. https://doi.org/10.3949/ccjm.76.s2.17

van Dernoot Lipsky, L. (2018). *The age of overwhelm: Strategies for the long haul.* Berrett-Koehler Publishers Inc.

Adaptive Leadership

Heifetz, R. A., Linsky, M., & Grashow, A. (2009). *The practice of adaptive leadership: Tools and tactics for changing your organization and the world.* Harvard Business Press.

Compassion Science

The Center for Compassion and Altruism Research and Education. (n.d.). *Mission & vision.* Stanford Medicine. http://ccare.stanford.edu/about/mission-vision/

Dev, V., Fernando, A. T., III, Lim, A. G., & Consedine, N. S. (2018). Does self-compassion mitigate the relationship between burnout and barriers to compassion? A cross-sectional quantitative study of 799 nurses. *International Journal of Nursing Studies, 81*, 81–88. https://doi.org/10.1016/j.ijnurstu.2018.02.003

Seppälä, E. M., Simon-Thomas, E., Brown, S. L., Worline, M. C., Cameron, C. D., & Doty, J. R. (2017). *The Oxford handbook of compassion science.* Oxford University Press.

Solitude

Nguyen, T. T., Weinstein, N., & Ryan, R. M. (2021). The possibilities of aloneness and solitude: Developing an understanding framed through the lens of human motivation and needs. In R. J. Coplan & J. C. Bowker (Eds.), *The handbook of solitude: Psychological perspectives on social isolation, social withdrawal, and being alone* (2nd ed., pp. 224–239). Wiley. https://doi.org/10.1002/9781119576457.ch16

Vital Leadership

Brown, B. (2019). *Dare to lead: Brave work, tough conversations, whole hearts.* Ebury Digital.

Levesque-Côté, J., Fernet, C., Morin, A. J. S., & Austin, S. (2020). On the motivational nature of authentic leadership practices: A latent profile analysis based on self-determination theory. *Leadership & Organization Development Journal, 42*(2), 178–194. https://doi.org/10.1108/LODJ-12-2019-0522

Shaw-VanBuskirk, L., Lim, D. H., & Jeong, S.-H. (2019), Liminal leadership: Leading betwixt and between. *European Journal of Training and Development, 43*(7/8), 643–660. https://doi.org/10.1108/EJTD-01-2019-0010

Uhl-Bien, M., Marion, R., & McKelvey, B. (2007). Complexity leadership theory: Shifting leadership from the industrial age to the knowledge era. *The Leadership Quarterly, 18*(4), 298–318. https://doi.org/10.1016/j.leaqua.2007.04.002

Emotional Regulation

Fosha, D. (2000). *The transforming power of affect: A model for accelerated change.* Basic Books.

Hendel, H. J. (2018). *It's not always depression: Working the change triangle to listen to the body, discover core emotions, and connect to your authentic self.* Spiegel & Grau.

Johnston, E., & Olson, L. (2015). *The feeling brain: The biology and psychology of emotions.* W. W. Norton & Company.

Roth, G., Vansteenkiste, M., & Ryan, R. M. (2019, May). Integrative emotion regulation: Process and development from a self-determination theory perspective. *Development and Psychopathology, 31*(3), 945–956. https://doi.org/10.1017/S0954579419000403

Timko Olson, E. R., Hansen, M. M., & Vermeesch, A. (2020). Mindfulness and shinrin-yoku: Potential for physiological and psychological interventions during uncertain times. *International Journal of Environmental Research and Public Health, 17*(24), Article 9340. https://doi.org/10.3390/ijerph17249340